BABY RECORD Book

Sue Warne

A souvenir of the first five years

Diamond

(Photograph)

Name

Born on _____

The Birth

Date _____

Time _____

Place _____

Delivered by _____

Weight _____

Length _____

Other details _____

_____

_____

*(Photograph of
baby and family)*

Family Tree

Mother

_____

Father

_____

Grandparents

_____

_____

Grandparents

_____

_____

Baby

_____

Brothers
and Sisters

_____

_____

_____

Newspaper Headlines

_____

_____

_____

_____

_____

_____

_____

First Visitors

_____

_____

_____

_____

_____

_____

_____

_____

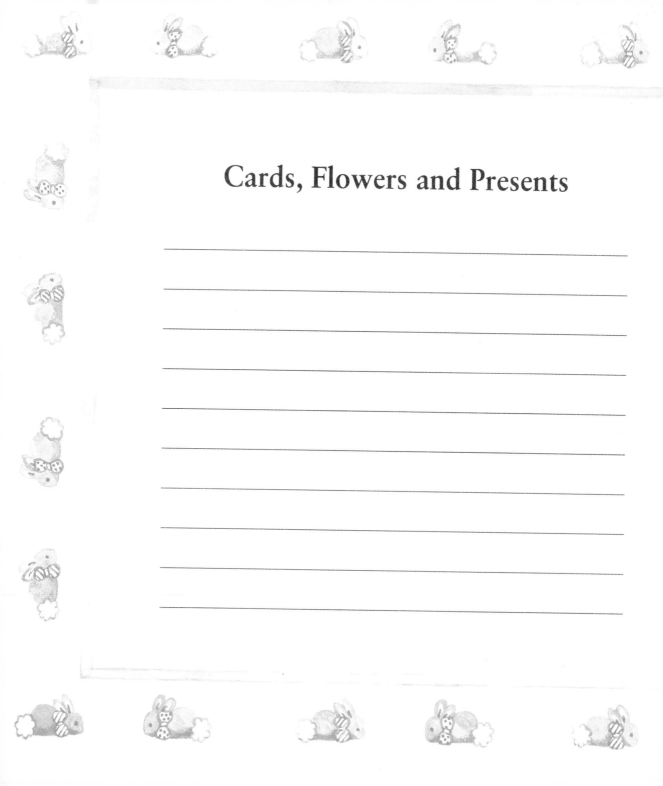

Cards, Flowers and Presents

_____

_____

_____

_____

_____

_____

_____

_____

_____

_____

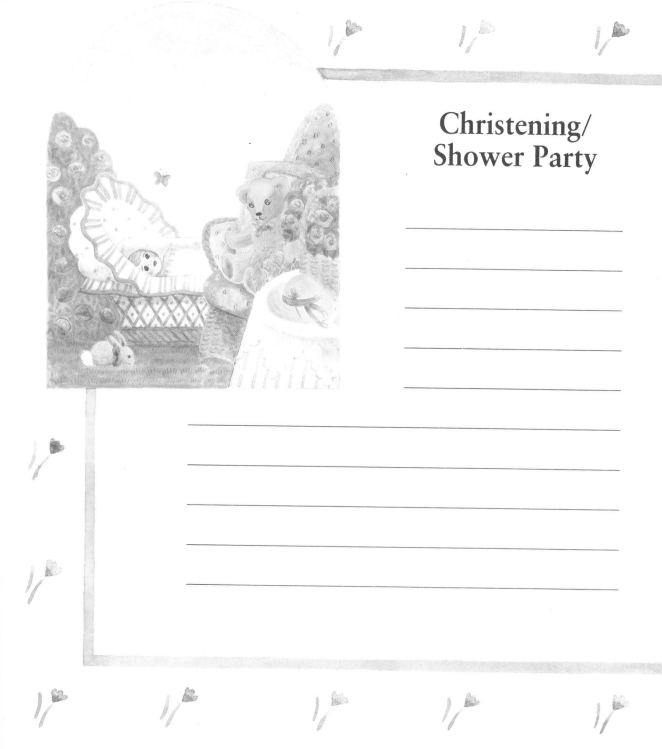

Christening/
Shower Party

Treasured Souvenirs

Birth announcements

Hospital bracelet

Lock of hair
(in a small envelope)

Identification Marks

Colour of eyes at birth _____

Colour of eyes at 1 year _____

Colour of hair at birth _____

Colour of hair at 1 year _____

Colour of eyelashes _____

Colour of eyebrows _____

Complexion _____

Special marks _____

(handprint)

(footprint)

Date _____

Baby's Firsts . . .

Smile _____

Laugh _____

Recognizes mother _____

Recognizes father _____

Notices strangers _____

Notices mobiles
and pictures _____

Early words _____

_____

_____

First phrases _____

_____

_____

More Firsts

Holds head up _____

Turns over _____

Sits up alone _____

Crawls _____

Stands _____

Walks _____

Climbs stairs _____

Runs _____

(Photograph)

More Firsts

First tooth _____

Eats solid foods _____

Begins to grasp objects _____

Waves goodbye _____

Other firsts _____

_____

_____

_____

_____

Favourite Things

Toys _____

_____

Books _____

_____

Games _____

_____

Rhymes/songs _____

_____

Foods _____

First Home

Address _____

_____

_____

(Photograph)

First Christmas

Spent at _____

(Photograph)

First Birthday

Guests _____

_____

_____

Gifts _____

_____

_____

Cake _____

(Photograph)

Funny Sayings

_____

_____

_____

_____

_____

_____

_____

Funny Deeds

_____

_____

_____

_____

_____

_____

_____

_____

Second Birthday

Guests _____

_____

_____

Gifts _____

_____

_____

Cake _____

(Photograph)

Early Drawings

(Stick in samples)

(Stick in samples)

Third Birthday

Guests _____

_____

_____

Gifts _____

_____

_____

Cake _____

(Photograph)

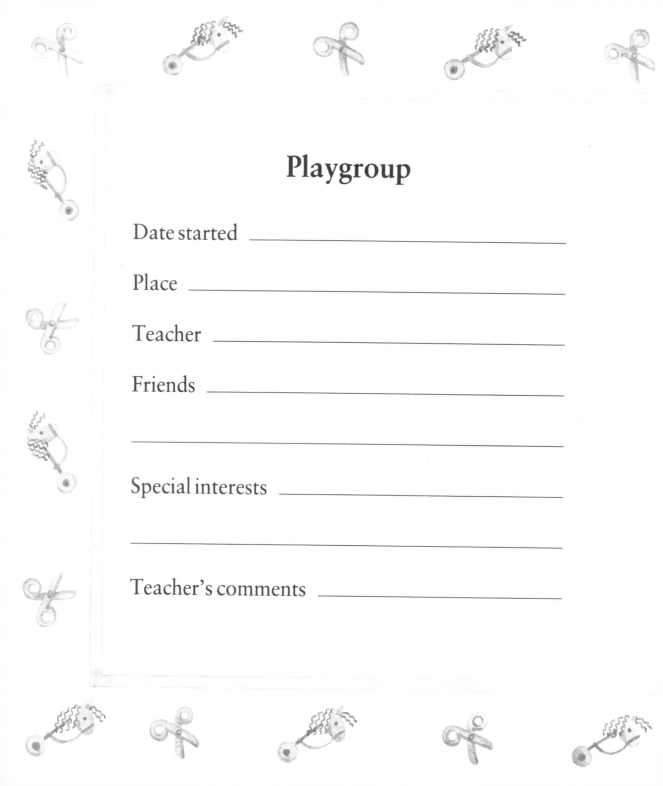

Playgroup

Date started _____

Place _____

Teacher _____

Friends _____

_____

Special interests _____

_____

Teacher's comments _____

(Photograph)

Favourite Books and Stories

First Writing

(Stick in samples)

First Writing

(Stick in samples)

Fourth Birthday

How celebrated _____

_____

_____

(Photograph)

Fifth Birthday

How celebrated _____

_____

_____

(Photograph)

Pets

_____

_____

_____

(Photograph)

(Photographs)

Off to School

Date started _____

School _____

Teacher _____

Friends _____

_____

Interests _____

Child's remarks _____

Teacher's notes _____

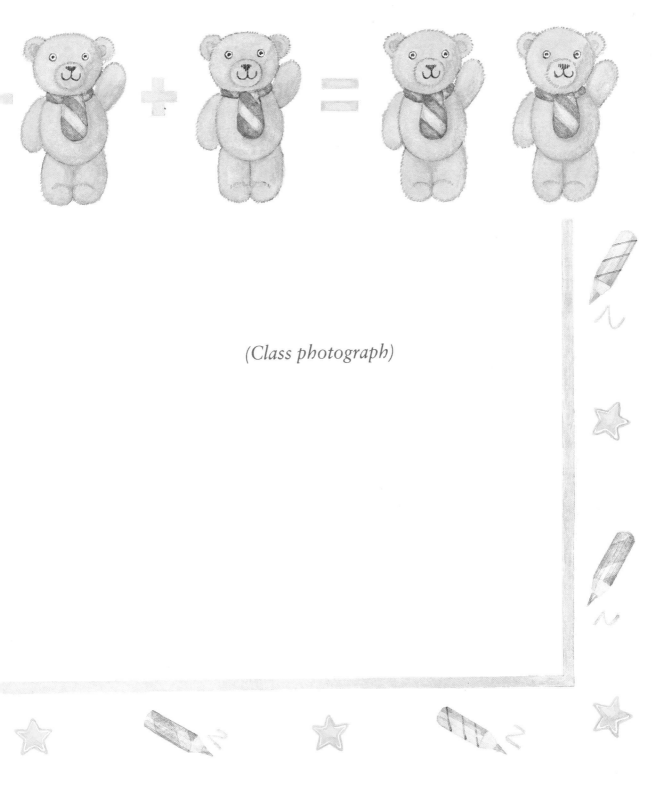

(Class photograph)

Injections, Illnesses and Allergies

_____

_____

_____

_____

_____

_____

_____

_____

Height and Weight

Age	Height	Weight

© 1988 Judy Piatkus (Designs) Limited

First published in 1988
by Diamond, an imprint of
Judy Piatkus (Designs) Limited,
5 Windmill Street, London W1P 1HF

Distributed in Canada by
McGraw-Hill Ryerson Limited
330 Progress Avenue
Scarborough M1P 2Z5

ISBN 1 871054 03 6

Illustration and design by Sue Warne

Phototypeset in Linotron Sabon by
Phoenix Photosetting, Chatham, Kent
Printed and bound in Hong Kong by
Imago Publishing, Thame, Oxon